Be the Change

Contribution by Kiyanni Bryan, Write It Out Publishing LLC in the United States of America.

Author: Lindsey Anderson
Illustrator: Haticeby Bayramoglu
Editor: Katherine A. Young

ISBN: 978-1-7377484-4-1
First Printing, 2021

Lindsey Anderson
Portsmouth, VA 23703
lindseyaofva@gmail.com

BE THE CHANGE!

written by
Lindsey Anderson

Write It Out Publishing LLC

Note to Reader

Hey friends!

When I was a little girl, I discovered my superpower. I'm a helper. I love to help people and be of service. It's something I do naturally that supports my community and those around me. As I've grown up, I've used my superpower to help people in need.

Can I tell you a secret? You have a superpower too. Everyone has a special gift that makes them unique, and they should want to share it with the world. Some people make beautiful art. Some people put out big fires. Some people teach children, and others are, like me, helpers. As you read this book, think about what you believe your superpower may be. Once you know, responsibly use your power as much as possible. I know you'll be a great superhero. Don't forget that you are never too small to Be The Change.

Lindsey Anderson

Dedication

This book is dedicated to Arria Britton. My heart, my motivator.

Sometimes, I hear and see things that are not right. My friends getting bullied, my brother is being yelled at, or even my mom falling asleep in her uniform after work because she's been working all night long.

I want to help, but what can I do? I'm small and too young. What if people don't hear me? What if they don't believe me? What can I do to fix things?

BE THE CHANGE!

What! Who said that?
What change?

How can I be the change?

Who I am is not important, but who you are and who you choose to be will make a world of difference.

If you want to BE THE CHANGE, you start by doing what is right, every chance you get. Help those in need. Speak up and speak out if you see something or someone doing wrong. Give back.
And most importantly, always be yourself.

Every one of us has a unique superpower that makes us special. Some people can make others look and feel good about themselves. Some people can empower others to be great. Some people are great listeners.

It's your job to figure out what your superpower is and how you can use it to make the place you live better.

But I'm still too little. The kids that bully my friend are way bigger than I am. The people who yell at my brother are adults. And I'm too young to work, so I can't help my mom.

If your friend is being bullied, tell an adult immediately. Stand by your friend's side so they know you are with them.

If you see an adult doing something you know is wrong, find an adult you trust to tell them the issue.

Even though you can't work yet, you can help your parents by following their instructions. You can even do nice things for your parents to make them smile. Saying "I love you" goes a very long way!

Wow! Those things don't seem too hard to do. I already hug my friends when they look sad. I didn't know those small things could really make a difference. So, if I do what's right, I will BE THE CHANGE?

Yes! That's exactly right. It is not hard to be the change, but it is a choice and every day you have to choose to do the right thing.

Once you start doing what's right, your friends and family around you will do the same. Change starts with YOU.

It doesn't matter how big or small you are, how young or old you are, or what you look like. We can all BE THE CHANGE.

"We are in this together"

Lindsey A of VA

A Message to The Community

Be the Change is not just a message for our youth; it's a call to action for everyone. Change is constant, meaning if we aren't happy with things today, there's always an opportunity to do something about it.

Now more than ever, our children need us. They need us to listen to them, they need us to see them, they need us to believe in them.
Our children need to know that every day is another opportunity to be better. Our children need to know that you can always get back up no matter how many times you get knocked down. Our children need to know that anything is possible. And most importantly, our children need to know that no matter what, someone will always be there for them.

We have to set a new example for our children. We have to provide them with safe spaces that allow them to find and operate in their superpower. We must show our children what it looks like to unify and work together. We must show our children what it looks like to communicate with each other and respect differences. We must show them what love looks like. We must show them what 'community' looks like.

It's never too late for change.

How can you "be the change" right now in your own community?

Be
the
CHANGE

What do you think is your superpower?

What's something you can do to make a change in your life?

Ingram Content Group UK Ltd.
Milton Keynes UK
UKHW052256190323
418795UK00003B/45